The Magic Num

GW00656305

Use the clues to cross out numbers. The number tho

1 It is not 5 + 1

2 It is not 12 – 7

3 It is not 3 + 1

4 It is not 3 + 9

5 It is not 10 – 8

6 It is not 6 + 2

7 It is not 15 – 12

8 It is not 7 + 4

The magic number is

_____!

5 4 12

2 8 11

3 6 7

3

Fishy Squares

Find all the hidden squares in each fish.

1 How many squares
do you see in this fish?

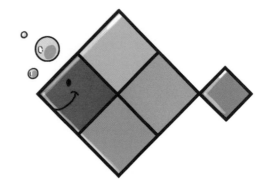

2 How many squares
do you see in this fish?

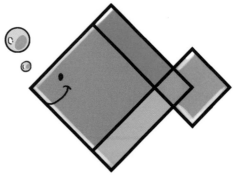

3 How many squares
do you see in this fish?

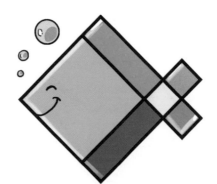

Why Math Puzzlers?

Research has shown that repetition is essential for the brain to learn and recall information. Furthermore, children have a tendency to repeat activities they enjoy. The engaging games and puzzles in this book will provide your child with repeated practice of grade-level-appropriate math skills. Continued practice with these skills helps develop a strong understanding of basic math concepts and builds a solid foundation in math problem solving, an important tool for academic success.

Upon your child's completion of each activity, use the provided incentive chart and stickers to track progress and celebrate your child's success.

SKILLS

- Numbers through 100
- Addition
- Subtraction
- Place value
- Money

- Shapes and solid figures
- Patterns
- Multistep word problems
- Logic and problem solving

HOW YOU CAN HELP SUPPORT LEARNING

- Encourage your child to use manipulatives, such as paper clips, beans, coins, and counting blocks, to model problems and connect meaning to the written words and symbols.
- Have your child draw pictures to represent the data or draw a number line to assist with addition and subtraction problems.
- Assist your child in identifying key math terms, such as *in all, altogether, sum, take away, from, difference, even, odd, equal, greater than*, and *less than*.
- Ask your child to explain his or her answers.
- Give hints rather than solutions to particularly tricky problems.
- Have your child check answers to addition and subtraction problems by working backward.

A Snowy Riddle

Add. Then write the letters that match the answers on the lines below.

6	8	10	12	14	16	18	20
K	B	S	I	A	W	N	O

Riddle

Where do snowmen keep their money?

6	10
+ 6	+ 8

6
+ 8

____ ____ ____

4	9	12	7	5	11	13	4
+ 6	+ 9	+ 8	+ 9	+ 3	+ 3	+ 5	+ 2

____ ____ ____ ____ ____ ____ ____ ____

Giraffe Mystery

Write the missing number for each addition sentence. Then
write the letters that match the answers on the lines below.

W	E	A	T	O
3 + ____ = 19	5 + ____ = 16	____ + 5 = 19	2 + ____ = 8	____ + 7 = 19
R	**M**	**H**	**F**	**N**
8 + ____ = 15	____ + 11 = 20	9 + ____ = 17	____ + 8 = 12	15 + ____ = 20

Riddle

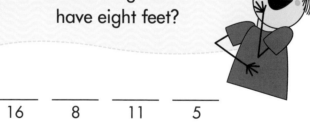

When do giraffes have eight feet?

____ ____ ____ ____
16   8   11   5

____ ____ ____ ____ ____
6   8   11   7   11

____ ____ ____   ____ ____ ____
14   7   11   6   16   12

____ ____   ____ ____ ____ ____
12   4   6   8   11   9

Shape Find

Find and circle the hidden shapes. Then complete the sentences below.

Key

triangle   square   rectangle   hexagon   circle

1 A ▲ is called a _____. I found _____ of them.

2 A ⬡ is called a _____. I found _____ of them.

3 A ◻ is called a _____. I found _____ of them.

4 A ● is called a _____. I found _____ of them.

5 A ▭ is called a _____. I found _____ of them.

Four Square

Look at the number puzzle and how the lines are shaped around each number. These line shapes are used in the problems below instead of numbers. For each problem, find the same line shapes in the number puzzle. Write those numbers and find the sum.

4	3
1	5

Hint: ⌐ = 4

---

1 ⌐ + ⌐ = ___

2 ⌐ + ⌐ = ___

3 ⌐ + ⌐ = ___

4 ⌐ + ⌐ = ___

5 ⌐ + ⌐ = ___

6 ⌐ + ⌐ = ___

7 ⌐ + ⌐ = ___

8 ⌐ + ⌐ = ___

9 ⌐ + ⌐ = ___

10 ⌐ + ⌐ = ___

All in the Family

Solve the problems to find out everyone's age.

1. Jim is 3 years older than his sister Kim. Their ages add up to 13.

   How old is Jim? _____

   How old is Kim? _____

2. Meg's mom is twice as old as Meg. Together, their ages add up to 60.

   How old is Meg? _____

   How old is Meg's mom? _____

3. Sandy and Mandy are twins. In two years, their ages will add up to 18.

   How old are the twins today? _____

The Lucky Number

Read the clues and cross out numbers to find the lucky number.

- I am greater than 9.
- The sum of my digits is 4.
- I am less than 21.
- The lucky number is _____.

1	2	3	4	5
6	7	8	9	10
11	12	13	14	15
16	17	18	19	20
21	22	23	24	25

Secret Numbers

Use the numbers in each set to write numbers that match the clues. Use each number only once.

1 The number is even.
It is greater than 35.
It is less than 50.

5
2
6
3

_____

2 The number is odd.
It is greater than 85.
It is less than 90.

9
8
2
5

_____

3 The number is even.
It is greater than 60.
It is less than 70.

3
7
6
2

_____

4 The number is even.
It is greater than 60.
It is less than 70.

4
6
7
9

_____

5 The number is even.
It is greater than 25.
It is less than 30.

2
8
4
3

_____

6 The number is odd.
It is greater than 80.
It is less than 95.

1
9
7
4

_____

7 The number is odd.
It is greater than 45.
It is less than 75.

3
9
4
2

_____

8 The number is even.
It is greater than 13.
It is less than 21.

8
2
3
1

_____

How Many Beads?

Anna put a cloth over each string of beads. Read the clues.
Then write how many beads are under each cloth.

1 There are 7 beads in all.

How many beads are
under the cloth? _____

2 There are 8 beads in all.

How many beads are
under the cloth? _____

3 There are 11 beads in all.

How many beads are
under the cloth? _____

4 There are 9 beads in all.

How many beads are
under the cloth? _____

5 There are 14 beads in all.

How many beads are
under the cloth? _____

6 There are 10 beads in all.

How many beads are
under the cloth? _____

Hocus, Pocus!

Use the numbers on each set of stars to help the wizard make three-digit numbers.

1 largest three-digit number _____

2 smallest three-digit number _____

3 largest three-digit number with 9 in the tens palce _____

5

3

9

. . . .

4 largest three-digit number _____

5 smallest three-digit number _____

6 largest three-digit number with the 6 in the ones place _____

4

6

1

. . . .

7 largest three-digit number _____

8 smallest three-digit number _____

9 largest three-digit number with the 7 in the ones place _____

8

2

7

On the Bus

Solve the problems.

1 There are 6 people on the bus. Then 2 people get off and 1 person gets on. How many people are on the bus now?

_____

2 There are 7 people on the bus. Then 4 people get off and 3 people get on. How many people are on the bus now?

_____

3 There are 10 people on the bus. The bus goes to 3 more stops. At each stop, 2 people get on. No one gets off. How many people are on the bus?

_____

4 There are 15 people on the bus. The bus goes to 2 more stops. At each stop, 4 people get off. How many people are on the bus now?

_____

5 There are 5 people on the bus. Then 6 people get on. At the next stop, some students get on. Now there are 15 people on the bus. How many students got on?

_____

6 There are 12 people on the bus. Then 5 people get off. At the next stop, some boy scouts get on. Now there are 14 people on the bus. How many boy scouts got on?

_____

What's in the Bag?

Draw the coins to show the correct combination.

1 There are 2 coins.
They add up to 15¢.

 10 **5**

2 There are 2 coins.
They add up to 35¢.

3 There are 3 coins.
They add up to 45¢.

4 There are 3 coins.
They add up to 25¢.

5 There are 3 coins.
They add up to 60¢.

6 There are 4 coins.
They add up to 60¢.

7 There are 4 coins.
They add up to 85¢.

8 There are 5 coins.
They add up to 65¢.

Time for a Riddle

Add. Then write the letters that match the answers on the lines below.

2	4	6	8	10	12	14
O	S	A	R	M	H	U

Riddle

What kind of room has no windows?

2 + 4	5 + 5	7 + 7	0 + 4	10 + 2	6 + 2	2 + 0	1 + 1	7 + 3

____ ____ ____ ____ ____ ____ ____ ____ ____

Here Comes the Circus!

Who's in the parade? Solve the problems to find out!

1 Steve counted the jugglers and bears in the parade. He counted 4 heads and 12 legs.

How many jugglers and bears were there?

_____ jugglers   _____ bears

. . . .

2 Matt counted the lion tamers and lions in the parade. He counted 5 heads and 16 legs.

How many lion tamers and lions were there?

_____ lion tamers   _____ lions

. . . .

3 Lori counted the clowns and elephants in the parade. She counted 7 heads and 20 legs.

How many clowns and elephants were there?

_____ clowns   _____ elephants

. . . .

4 Chelsea counted the acrobats and horses in the parade. She counted 8 heads and 24 legs.

How many acrobats and horses were there?

_____ acrobats   _____ horses

Find the Robot

Read the clues and write the number of the matching robot for each one.

1   2   3   4

1 I have two squares for my feet. My hands match the shape on my chest.

_____

2 My head is a rectangle. I have two circles for my feet.

_____

3 I have four triangles on my body. My hands match the shape on my chest.

_____

4 I have two squares for my feet. I have rectangles on my chest.

_____

5 Draw a robot made of shapes. Write two sentences describing your robot.

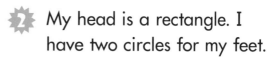

_____

_____

_____

Apple Subtraction

Find the differences. Color all the even answers **red** and all the odd answers **green**.

12
− 8

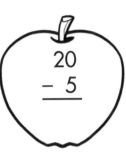

20
− 5

13
− 9

19
− 5

14
− 7

16
− 9

15
− 4

20
− 6

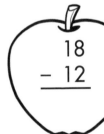

18
− 12

11
− 7

17
− 9

10
− 9

Guess Ethan's Number

Use the clues to cross out numbers. The number that is left is Ethan's number.

- The number has two digits.
- Each digit is less than 6.
- The sum of my digits is 8.
- The number is even.
- Ethan's number is _____.

1	2	3	4	5	6	7	8	9	10
11	12	13	14	15	16	17	18	19	20
21	22	23	24	25	26	27	28	29	30
31	32	33	34	35	36	37	38	39	40
41	42	43	44	45	46	47	48	49	50
51	52	53	54	55	56	57	58	59	60
61	62	63	64	65	66	67	68	69	70
71	72	73	74	75	76	77	78	79	80
81	82	83	84	85	86	87	88	89	90
91	92	93	94	95	96	97	98	99	100

Super Spaceships

Write the numbers from the box in the squares below so that the sum of each row is **10**.

| 1 | 2 | 3 | 4 | 5 |

Number Riddles

Circle the correct answer for each number riddle.

1 I have 4 tens and 3 ones. What number am I?

34   43   42

2 I have 6 tens and 0 ones. What number am I?

6   600   60

3 I have 5 ones and 1 ten. What number am I?

63   15   35

4 I have 3 tens and 3 ones. What number am I?

3   33   30

5 I have 8 tens and 3 ones. What number am I?

38   83   88

6 I have 2 ones and 6 tens. What number am I?

26   62   20

7 I have 1 ten and 7 ones. What number am I?

11   17   18

8 I have 6 ones and 2 tens. What number am I?

62   206   26

Sly Foxes

Use the clues to cross out numbers and find the fox that has the secret number.

1 It is not 10 + 2.

2 It is not 6 + 7.

3 It is not 4 + 12.

4 It is not 6 + 5.

5 It is not 9 + 6.

6 It is not 7 + 10.

7 It is not 2 + 8.

8 It is not 9 + 9.

9 It is not 8 + 6.

The secret number is _____ .

Hidden Solid Shapes

Find and circle the hidden solid shapes from the Key. Then complete the sentences below.

Key

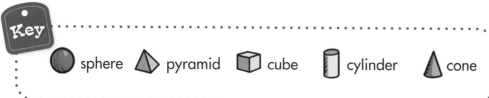

sphere   pyramid   cube   cylinder   cone

A ⬤ is called a _____ . I found _____ of them.

A 🔺 is called a _____ . I found _____ of them.

A ⬜ is called a _____ . I found _____ of them.

A ▯ is called a _____ . I found _____ of them.

A 🔺 is called a _____ . I found _____ of them.

Coin Patterns

Solve each problem.

 Jake had 10 coins. He started laying them in a pattern like this:

How much money did Jake have? To find out, label the coins and write the amount.

⑤ ⑩ ◯ ◯ ◯ ◯ ◯ ◯ ◯ ◯ = _____ ¢

 Kim had 10 coins. She started laying them in a pattern like this:

How much money did Kim have? To find out, label the coins and write the amount.

◯ ◯ ◯ ◯ ◯ ◯ ◯ ◯ ◯ ◯ = _____ ¢

 Julius had 10 coins. He started laying them in a pattern like this:

How much money did Julius have? To find out, label the coins and write the amount.

◯ ◯ ◯ ◯ ◯ ◯ ◯ ◯ ◯ ◯ = _____ ¢

Bear Buddies

Find out which bears are together. There are 6 teddy bears. Each one is a different color. Read the clues. Then color the pictures to show how the bears are paired up.

- The **brown** bear is with either the yellow bear or the **black** bear.

- The orange bear is with either the **black** bear or the **purple** bear.

- The **blue** bear is with the **purple** bear.

Who's Who?

Read the clues and write each child's name under the correct picture.

 Clues:

- Sid is taller than Jim.
- Tom is taller than Jim.
- Sid is taller than Tom.

_____   _____   _____

 Clues:

- Sue is taller than Dee.
- Bev is taller than Jan.
- Jan is taller than Sue.

_____   _____   _____   _____

Number Sentence Words

Find and circle the words from the Word Box.

Word Box

add	subtract	minus	difference
equal	answer	sum	plus

```
d  i  f  f  e  r  e  n  c  e
y  t  l  o  n  q  m  d  t  x
u  w  n  p  m  c  i  x  m  w
a  b  x  l  a  h  n  y  w  a
d  o  z  u  y  u  u  m  f  n
d  h  s  s  z  r  s  i  b  s
x  n  p  q  v  o  b  r  z  w
c  s  u  b  t  r  a  c  t  e
z  u  z  e  u  a  e  k  y  r
t  m  d  n  e  q  u  a  l  z
```

Hidden Symbols

Find and circle the hidden operation symbols from the Key. Then complete the sentences below.

1 A < is called a _____ sign. I found _____ of them.

2 A + is called a _____ sign. I found _____ of them.

3 A > is called a _____ sign. I found _____ of them.

4 A = is called an _____ sign. I found _____ of them.

5 A − is called a _____ sign. I found _____ of them.

Dot-to-Dots

Connect the dots to extend each pattern. Then connect the dots to make your own pattern.

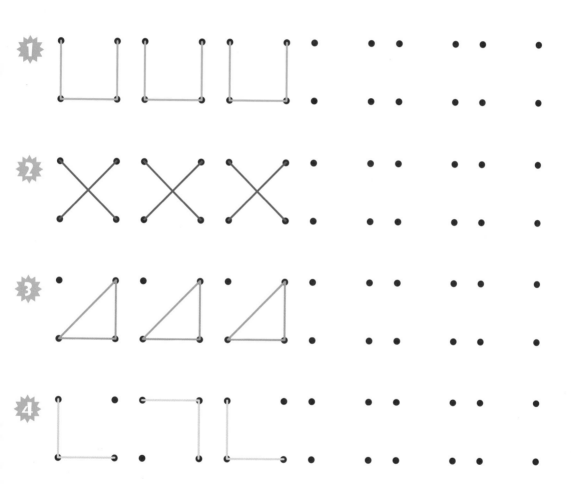

The Secret Doughnut Code

Subtract and write the letters that match the answers on the lines to solve the riddle.

0	1	2	3	4	5	6	7	8	9	10
N	T	I	H	F	E	A	O	L	C	G

Riddle

Why did the doughnut go to the dentist?

9 − 8	14 − 7

12 − 2	9 − 4	6 − 5

10 − 4

_____ _____   _____ _____ _____   _____

17 − 8	12 − 9	15 − 8	16 − 7	13 − 6	11 − 3	12 − 6	9 − 8	11 − 6

_____ _____ _____ _____ _____ _____ _____ _____ _____

13 − 9	10 − 8	14 − 6	16 − 8	11 − 9	10 − 10	15 − 5

_____ _____ _____ _____ _____ _____ _____

Time Puzzlers

Solve the problems.

1

Neil has a baseball game at 3:00. It will take him half an hour to get to the park. What time does Neil have to leave home to get to the park by 3:00?

_____

2

A movie ended at 8:00. It lasted 2½ hours. What time did the movie start?

_____

3

Kenny gets up every morning at 7:00. He always has 10 hours of sleep. What time does Kenny go to bed?

_____

4

Wendy's school starts at 8:30. It takes her 15 minutes to walk to school. What is the latest time that Wendy can leave home?

_____

Cowboys and Horses

Some cowboys took their horses on a trail ride. Altogether, there were 10 heads and 36 legs. How many cowboys and how many horses were there? Draw a picture to help you find the answer.

_____ cowboys   _____ horses

Six Square

Look at the number puzzle and see how the lines are shaped around each number. These line shapes are used in the problems below instead of numbers. For each problem, find the same line shapes in the number puzzle. Write those numbers and find the sum.

2	4	1
3	5	8

Example: 8 + 1 = _9_

1. ___ + ___ = ___

2. ___ + ___ = ___

3. ___ + ___ = ___

4. ___ + ___ = ___

5. ___ + ___ = ___

6. ___ + ___ = ___

7. ___ + ___ = ___

8. ___ + ___ = ___

9. ___ + ___ = ___

10. ___ + ___ = ___

Plus and Minus Puzzler

Write **+** or **−** in the circles to make the two number sentences equal.

1   3 ◯ 5 = 9 ◯ 1   **2**   6 ◯ 6 = 9 ◯ 3

3   11 ◯ 4 = 12 ◯ 5   **4**   13 ◯ 5 = 6 ◯ 2

5   6 ◯ 4 = 8 ◯ 6   **6**   11 ◯ 2 = 3 ◯ 6

7   8 ◯ 5 = 7 ◯ 6   **8**   10 ◯ 6 = 12 ◯ 8

9   10 ◯ 5 = 2 ◯ 3   **10**   7 ◯ 3 = 2 ◯ 8

Guess Benny's Number

Benny is thinking of a number. Read the clues to find out what it is. As you read each clue, cross off the numbers on the chart. At the end, you will be left with Benny's number.

- The number has two digits.
- Both digits are greater than or equal to 5.
- The tens digit is greater than the ones digit.
- The sum of the digits is 12.

Benny's number is _____ .

1	2	3	4	5	6	7	8	9	10
11	12	13	14	15	16	17	18	19	20
21	22	23	24	25	26	27	28	29	30
31	32	33	34	35	36	37	38	39	40
41	42	43	44	45	46	47	48	49	50
51	52	53	54	55	56	57	58	59	60
61	62	63	64	65	66	67	68	69	70
71	72	73	74	75	76	77	78	79	80
81	82	83	84	85	86	87	88	89	90
91	92	93	94	95	96	97	98	99	100

Fun on the Farm

Add. Then write the letters that match the answers on the lines to solve the riddle.

0	1	2	3	4	5	6	7
G	O	E	B	N	R	I	H

Riddle

What did the horse say when he moved into the barn?

4 +3	5 +1		2 +2	1 +1	4 +2	0 +0	3 +4	1 +2	0 +1	0 +5

"_____ _____"
—

____ ____

____ ____ ____ ____ ____ ____ ____

Solid Figures

Write the names of the solid shapes to complete the crossword puzzle.

cone   cube   cylinder   pyramid   sphere

Across

2.

3.

4.

Down

1.

2.

Who Am I?

Read the clues and write the correct name on each line.

Lori

Ricky

Stacy

Evan

Rachel

Max

1. I am older than 10.
I am not a girl.

_____

2. I am 2 years older than
the youngest boy.

_____

3. I am 5 years younger
than the oldest girl.

_____

4. I am older than Lori. I
am younger than Evan.

_____

5. I am older than Ricky. I
am younger than Rachel.

_____

6. I am 1 year older than
the youngest girl.

_____

The Great Pie Bake-Off

There are 6 pies in the bake-off. The flavors are apple, blueberry, and cherry. Read the clues. Then label the pies.

- There are more cherry pies than apple pies.
- There are more blueberry pies than cherry pies.

_____

_____

_____

_____

_____

_____

A Spooky Riddle

Subtract. Then write the answers in the boxes below the problems. To solve the riddle, write the letters that match the answers on the lines below.

1	2	3	4	5	6	7	8	9
O	E	T	C	H	S	F	G	I

Riddle

Where do ghosts go to mail their letters?

9 − 6	10 − 5	5 − 3

8 − 0	7 − 2	10 − 9	10 − 4	8 − 5

____ ____ ____   ____ ____ ____ ____ ____

9 − 8	10 − 3	8 − 1	9 − 0	10 − 6	7 − 5

____ ____ ____ ____ ____ ____

Zoo Clues

Read the clues to find out how many zoo animals the children saw.

1 Cindy saw some parrots and camels. She counted 4 heads and 12 feet. How many parrots and camels did Cindy see?

_____ parrots   _____ camels

2 Evan saw some ostriches and hippos. He counted 5 heads and 14 feet. How many ostriches and hippos did Evan see?

_____ ostriches   _____ hippos

3 Joann saw some ducks and deer. She counted 7 heads and 18 feet. How many ducks and deer did Joanne see?

_____ ducks   _____ deer

4 Randy saw some peacocks and tigers. He counted 7 heads and 22 feet. How many peacocks and tigers did Randy see?

_____ peacocks   _____ tigers

Perfect Aim!

Look at the number in the center of each target. Next, look at a number in the outside ring. Then decide what number must be added to the center number to equal the outside number. Write that number in the inside ring.

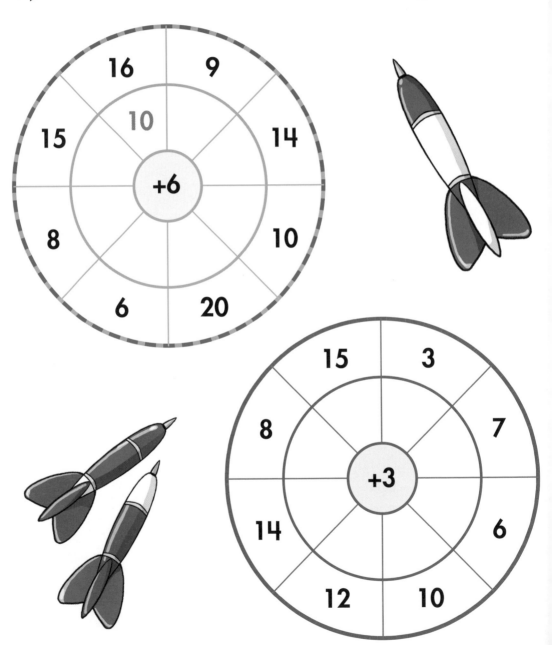

© 2012 CTP - 7223

What's My Number?

Solve the number riddles, and circle the correct answers.

1 I have 1 ten and 6 ones.
What number am I?

61   16

2 I have 3 tens and 2 ones.
What number am I?

32   23

3 I have 9 ones and less than 4
tens. What number am I?

49   29

4 I have 2 ones and more than 6
tens. What number am I?

72   52

5 I have 8 tens and more than 7
ones. What number am I?

89   86

6 I have 4 tens and less than 5
ones. What number am I?

47   43

7 I have less than 7 ones and more
than 5 tens. What number am I?

55   61

8 I have more than 3 ones and less
than 7 tens. What number am I?

88   56

Which Letter?

Color the problems in each row that have the answer on the left. If your answers are correct, you will form a letter. Write the letter at the bottom of the page.

11	5 + 6	8 + 2	5 + 4	6 + 7	7 + 4
16	9 + 5	10 + 6	2 + 7	8 + 8	4 + 9
12	6 + 7	13 + 2	4 + 8	3 + 8	4 + 6
10	4 + 7	3 + 9	6 + 4	7 + 7	9 + 2
14	6 + 6	7 + 5	5 + 9	9 + 6	8 + 7

What letter did you make? _____

Spider Web Puzzle

Write the numbers from the box below in the empty squares so that the sum of each row is **17**. One number will be left over.

1 2 3 4 5 6 7 8 9 10 11

5

Bull's Eye!

Look at the number in the center of each target. Next, look at a number in the outside ring. Then decide what number must be added to the center number to equal the outside number. Write that number in the inside ring.

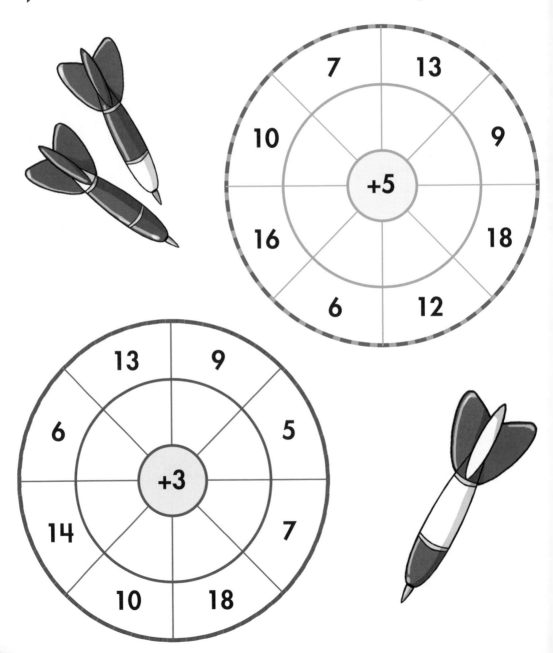

Pigs on the Go!

Write the missing number for each addition sentence. To solve the riddle, write the letters that match the answers on the lines below.

T	I	S	N	P
6 + ____ = 13	____ + 9 = 13	8 + ____ = 13	10 + ____ = 13	7 + ____ = 13
G	**U**	**C**	**R**	**K**
5 + ____ = 13	____ + 4 = 13	3 + ____ = 13	11 + ____ = 13	12 + ____ = 13

Riddle

How do pigs travel?

____ ____   ____ ____ ____ – ____ ____
 4   3   6   4   8   9   6

____ ____ ____ ____ ____ ____
 7   2   9   10   1   5

Fishing Fun

Sam caught 8 fish. They are **red**, **blue**, and yellow.
Read the clues. Then color the fish.

 Clues

- There is one more yellow fish than **blue** fish.
- There are more **red** fish than yellow fish.

Waiting in Line

Use the pictures to answer the questions. Then write the children's names below their pictures.

_____ _____ _____ _____ _____

1 Cory is second in line.
How many children are behind him?

2 Dana is fifth in line.
How many children are in front of her?

3 Jan is fourth in line.
How many children are behind her?

4 Susie is first in line.
How many children are behind her?

5 Alex is third in line. How many children
are between Alex and Dana?

Dru's Clues

Dru wrote some number riddles. Read the clues.
Then write the answer to each riddle.

1 The number is greater than 40 and less than 60. Count by tens, and you say the number.

The number is _____ .

2 The number is greater than 60 and less than 70. Count by fives, and you say number.

The number is _____ .

3 The number is greater than 35 and less than 45. Count by fives, and you say the number.

The number is _____ .

4 The number is greater than 12 and less than 16. Count by twos, and you say the number.

The number is _____ .

5 The number is greater than 15 and less than 20. Count by threes, and you say the number.

The number is _____ .

6 The number is greater than 20 and less than 25. Count by fours, and you say the number.

The number is _____ .

A Day at the Fair

Look at the price of each item. Then solve the problems.

flag 25¢   balloon 20¢   ice cream 50¢   monkey 75¢   clown 80¢

1 David has 2 dimes. What can he buy?

_____

 2 Elise has 5 dimes. How many flags can she buy?

_____

3 Jenna has 2 quarters. What is the most expensive item she can buy?

_____

 4 Marcus has 3 quarters. What is the most expensive thing he can buy?

_____

5 Paul has 2 quarters. How much more money does he need to buy the clown?

_____

 6 Jessica has 2 quarters and 2 nickels. How much more money does she need to buy the monkey?

_____

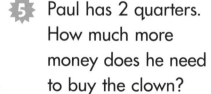 **7** Kim has 3 quarters. How many balloons can she buy?

_____

 8 Matt has 2 quarters and 2 dimes. Does he have enough to buy the monkey?

_____

Answer Key

PAGE 2

PAGE 3

PAGE 4
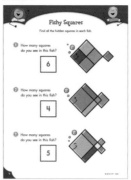

PAGE 5

PAGE 6

PAGE 7

PAGE 8

PAGE 9

PAGE 10

PAGE 11
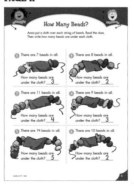

PAGE 12

PAGE 13
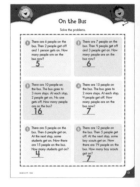

What's in the Bag?

Draw the coins to show the correct combination.

1. There are 2 coins. They add up to 15¢.
2. There are 2 coins. They add up to 35¢.
3. There are 3 coins. They add up to 45¢.
4. There are 3 coins. They add up to 25¢.
5. There are 3 coins. They add up to 60¢.
6. There are 4 coins. They add up to 60¢.
7. There are 4 coins. They add up to 85¢.
8. There are 5 coins. They add up to 65¢.

Time for a Riddle

Add. Then write the letters that match the answers on the lines below.

2	4	6	8	10	12	14
O	S	A	R	M	H	U

What kind of room has no windows?

A MUSHROOM

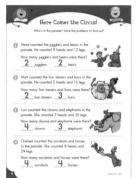

Here Comes the Circus!

Who's in the parade? Solve the problems to find out!

1. Steve counted the jugglers and bears in the parade. He counted 4 heads and 12 legs. How many jugglers and bears were there?
   2 jugglers 2 bears

2. Matt counted the lion tamers and lions in the parade. He counted 5 heads and 16 legs. How many lion tamers and lions were there?
   2 lion tamers 3 lions

3. Lori counted the clowns and elephants in the parade. She counted 7 heads and 20 legs. How many clowns and elephants were there?
   4 clowns 3 elephants

4. Chelsea counted the acrobats and horses in the parade. She counted 8 heads and 24 legs. How many acrobats and horses were there?
   4 acrobats 4 horses

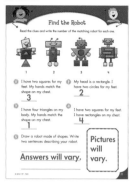

Find the Robot

Read the clues and write the number of the matching robot for each one.

1. I have two squares for my feet. My hands match the shape on my chest. 3
2. My head is a rectangle. I have two circles for my feet. 2
3. I have four triangles on my body. My hands match the shape on my chest. 1
4. I have two squares for my feet. I have rectangles on my chest. 4
5. Draw a robot made of shapes. Write two sentences describing your robot.
   Answers will vary. Pictures will vary.

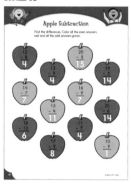

Apple Subtraction

Find the differences. Color all the even answers red and all the odd answers green.

12 − 8 = 4
20 − 5 = 15
19 − 5 = 14
13 − 8 = 5
16 − 9 = 7
14 − 7 = 7
15 − 4 = 11
20 − 6 = 14
18 − 12 = 6
11 − 7 = 4
12 − 4 = 8
10 − 9 = 1

Guess Ethan's Number

Use the clues to cross out numbers. The number that is left is Ethan's number.

- The number has two digits.
- Each digit is less than 6.
- The sum of my digits is 8.
- The number is even.
- Ethan's number is 44

44

Super Spaceships

Write the numbers from the box in the squares below so that the sum of each row is 10.

1 2 3 4 5

3
4
5
1
2

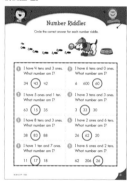

Number Riddles

Circle the correct answer for each number riddle.

1. I have 4 tens and 3 ones. What number am I? 34 43 42
2. I have 6 tens and 0 ones. What number am I? 6 600 60
3. I have 5 ones and 1 ten. What number am I? 63 15 35
4. I have 3 tens and 3 ones. What number am I? 3 33 30
5. I have 8 tens and 3 ones. What number am I? 38 83 88
6. I have 2 ones and 6 tens. What number am I? 26 62 20
7. I have 1 ten and 7 ones. What number am I? 11 17 18
8. I have 6 ones and 2 tens. What number am I? 62 206 26

Sly Foxes

Use the clues to cross out numbers and find the fox that has the secret number.

1. It is not 10 + 2.
2. It is not 6 + 7.
3. It is not 4 + 12.
4. It is not 6 + 5.
5. It is not 9 + 6.
6. It is not 7 + 10.
7. It is not 7 + 8.
8. It is not 9 + 9.
9. It is not 8 + 6.

The secret number is 19.

Hidden Solid Shapes

Find and circle the hidden solid shapes from the Key. Then complete the sentences below.

Key: sphere pyramid cube cylinder cone

A ___ is called a sphere. I found 7 of them.
A ___ is called a pyramid. I found 5 of them.
A ___ is called a cube. I found 5 of them.
A ___ is called a cylinder. I found 4 of them.
A ___ is called a cone. I found 3 of them.

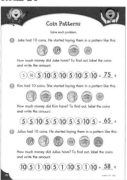

Coin Patterns

Solve each problem.

1. Jake had 10 coins. He started laying them in a pattern like this:
   How much money did Jake have? To find out, label the coins and write the amount.
   5 10 5 10 5 10 5 10 5 10 = 75¢

2. Kim had 10 coins. She started laying them in a pattern like this:
   How much money did Kim have? To find out, label the coins and write the amount.
   5 5 10 5 5 10 5 5 10 5 = 65¢

3. Julius had 10 coins. He started laying them in a pattern like this:
   How much money did Julius have? To find out, label the coins and write the amount.
   10 5 1 10 5 1 10 5 1 10 = 58¢

Bear Buddies

Find out which bears are together. There are 6 teddy bears. Each one is a different color. Read the clues. Then color the pictures to show how the bears are paired up.

- The brown bear is with either the yellow bear or the black bear.
- The orange bear is with either the black bear or the purple bear.
- The blue bear is with the purple bear.

Who's Who?

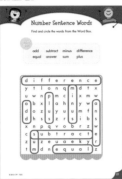

Number Sentence Words

Hidden Symbols

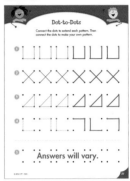

Dot-to-Dots

The Secret Doughnut Code

Time Puzzlers

Cowboys and Horses

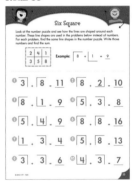

Six Square

Plus and Minus Puzzler

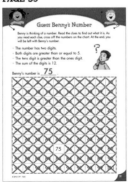

Guess Benny's Number

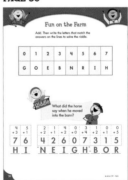

Fun on the Farm

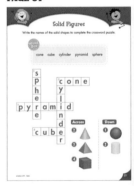

Solid Figures

Who Am I?

Read the clues and write the correct name on each line.

Lori 4   Ricky 6   Stacy 11

Evan 12   Rachel ?   Max ?

1. I am older than 10. I am not a girl.
   Evan
2. I am 2 years older than the youngest boy.
   Rachel
3. I am 5 years younger than the oldest girl.
   Ricky
4. I am older than Evan.
   Stacy
5. I am older than Ricky. I am younger than Rachel.
   Max
6. I am 1 year older than the youngest girl.
   Lori

The Great Pie Bake-Off

There are 6 pies in the bake-off. The flavors are apple, blueberry, and cherry. Read the clues. Then label the pies.

Clues
- There are more cherry pies than apple pies.
- There are more blueberry pies than cherry pies.

blueberry   blueberry

blueberry

cherry

cherry

apple

A Spooky Riddle

Subtract. Then write the answers in the boxes below the problems. To solve the riddle, write the letters that match the answers on the lines below.

1	2	3	4	5	6	7	8	9
O	E	T	C	H	S	F	G	I

Where do ghosts go to mail their letters?

9	10	5		8	7	10	8
−6	−5	−3		−0	−2	−9	−4
3	5	2		8	5	1	6	3

T H E   G H O S T

9	10	8	9	10	7
−8	−3	−1	−0	−6	−5
1	7	7	9	4	2

O F F I C E

Zoo Clues

Read the clues to find out how many zoo animals the children saw.

1. Cindy saw some parrots and camels. She counted 4 heads and 12 feet. How many parrots and camels did Cindy see?
   2 parrots   **2** camels
2. Evan saw some ostriches and hippos. He counted 5 heads and 14 feet. How many ostriches and hippos did Evan see?
   3 ostriches   **2** hippos
3. Joann saw some ducks and deer. She counted 7 heads and 18 feet. How many ducks and deer did Joanne see?
   5 ducks   **2** deer
4. Randy saw some peacocks and tigers. He counted 7 heads and 22 feet. How many peacocks and tigers did Randy see?
   3 peacocks   **4** tigers

Perfect Aim!

Look at the number in the center of each target. Next, look at a number in the outside ring. Then decide what number must be added to the center number to equal the outside number. Write that number in the inside ring.

What's My Number?

Solve the number riddles, and circle the correct answers.

1. I have 1 ten and 6 ones. What number am I?   61   **16**
2. I have 3 tens and 2 ones. What number am I?   **32**   23
3. I have 9 ones and less than 4 tens. What number am I?   49   **29**
4. I have 2 ones and more than 6 tens. What number am I?   **72**   52
5. I have 8 tens and more than 7 ones. What number am I?   **89**   86
6. I have 4 tens and less than 5 ones. What number am I?   47   **43**
7. I have less than 7 ones and more than 5 tens. What number am I?   55   **61**
8. I have more than 3 ones and less than 7 tens. What number am I?   88   **56**

Which Letter?

Color the problems in each row that have the answer on the left. If your answers are correct, you will form a letter. Write the letter at the bottom of the page.

11	5+6	8+2	5+4	6+7	7+4
16	9+5	10+6	2+7	9+7	8+8
12	6+7	13+2	4+8	3+8	4+6
10	4+7	3+9	6+4	7+7	9+2
14	6+6	7+5	5+9	9+6	8+7

What letter did you make? **Y**

Spider Web Puzzle

Write the numbers from the box below in the empty squares so that the sum of each row is 17. One number will be left over.

| 1 | 2 | 3 | 4 | 5 | 6 | 7 | 8 | 9 | 10 | 11 |

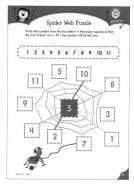

11   5   10   8
9   5   3
4   2   7   1

Bull's Eye!

Look at the number in the center of each target. Next, look at a number in the outside ring. Then decide what number must be added to the center number to equal the outside number. Write that number in the inside ring.

Pigs on the Go!

Write the missing number for each addition sentence. To solve the riddle, write the letters that match the answers on the lines below.

I   T   I   S   N   P
6+**7**=13   **4**+9=13   6+**5**=13   10+**3**=13   7+**6**=13

G   U   R   C   K   S
5+**8**=13   **9**+4=13   3+**10**=13   11+**2**=13   12+**1**=13

How do pigs travel?

I N   P I G U P
4   7   9   2   10   5

T R U C K S
1   7   9   10   1   5

Fishing Fun

Sam caught 8 fish. They are red, blue, and yellow. Read the clues. Then color the fish.

Clues
- There is one more yellow fish than blue fish.
- There are more red fish than yellow fish.

Waiting in Line

Use the pictures to answer the questions. Then write the children's names below their pictures.

Susie   Cory   Alex   Jan   Dana

1. Cory is second in line. How many children are behind him? **3**
2. Dana is fifth in line. How many children are in front of her? **4**
3. Jan is fourth in line. How many children are behind her? **1**
4. Susie is first in line. How many children are behind her? **4**
5. Alex is third in line. How many children are between Alex and Dana? **1**

Dru's Clues

Dru wrote some number riddles. Read the clues. Then write the answer to each riddle.

1. The number is greater than 40 and less than 60. Count by tens, and you say the number.

The number is __50__

2. The number is greater than 60 and less than 70. Count by fives, and you say number.

The number is __65__

3. The number is greater than 35 and less than 45. Count by fives, and you say the number.

The number is __40__

4. The number is greater than 12 and less than 16. Count by twos, and you say the number.

The number is __14__

5. The number is greater than 15 and less than 20. Count by threes, and you say the number.

__18__

6. The number is greater than 20 and less than 25. Count by fours, and you say the number.

__24__

A Day at the Fair

Look at the price of each item. Then solve the problems.

flag 25¢   balloon 20¢   ice cream 50¢   monkey 75¢   clown 80¢

1. David has 2 dimes. What can he buy?
__balloon__

2. Elise has 5 dimes. How many flags can she buy?
__2__

3. Jenna has 2 quarters. What is the most expensive item she can buy?
__ice cream__

4. Marcus has 3 quarters. What is the most expensive thing he can buy?
__monkey__

5. Paul has 2 quarters. How much more money does he need to buy the clown?
__30¢__

6. Jessica has 2 quarters and 2 nickels. How much more money does she need to buy the monkey?
__15¢__

7. Kim has 3 quarters. How many balloons can she buy?
__3__

8. Matt has 2 quarters and 2 dimes. Does he have enough to buy the monkey?
__no__